To those for whom and to whom I'm most grateful: my parents, who raised me in a loving and nurturing environment; my husband, who is my biggest supporter and cheerleader; and my children, who are my inspiration and who teach me new things daily.

Publisher's Cataloging-in-Publication data

Names: Mendoza-Vasconez, Andrea Susana, author. | Nilson, Rita, illustrator.
Title: The gratitude goggles / by Andrea Mendoza-Vasconez, PhD; illustrated by Rita Nilson.
Series: Wholesome Children: Self-Awareness
Description: San Diego, CA: Wholesome Children Books LLC, 2023. | Summary: Children imagine a special pair of goggles that can appear by simply feeling gratitude, and that reveal the world in its true, colorful splendor.
Identifiers: LCCN: 2023917158 | ISBN: 979-8-9880229-5-4 (hardcover) | 979-8-9880229-4-7 (paperback) | 979-8-9880229-6-1 (Kindle) | 979-8-9880229-7-8 (epub)
Subjects: LCSH Gratitude--Juvenile fiction. | Happiness--Juvenile fiction. | Emotions--Juvenile fiction. | BISAC JUVENILE FICTION / Imagination & Play | JUVENILE FICTION / Social Themes / Emotions & Feelings | JUVENILE FICTION / Social Themes / Values & Virtues
Classification: LCC PZ7.1 .M46 Gr 2023 | DDC [E]--dc23

Andrea Mendoza-Vasconez, PhD

Illustrated by Rita Nilson

The Gratitude Goggles

Let's play make-believe!

Imagine that you are wearing gray goggles... and everything you look at appears to be dull and gray.

If you look around with your gray goggles, you may feel that something is missing in your life.

You might not know exactly what is wrong, but things just don't feel right.

You might feel like comparing yourself to others...
Do they have something that you don't have?

Why do they look so beautiful and happy?
Why does their life seem to be full of color,
when yours looks just...gray?

When people feel this way, they may try to change themselves to look like others.

They may also feel tempted to buy many new things to see if that brings some color back into their lives.

But if you focus on what you **don't** have, instead of focusing on what you **do** have, the colors around you will only get darker and darker gray.

What happens when you take the gray goggles off...
or switch them for gratitude goggles instead?

GOGGLES

While goggles come in many shapes and colors,
the gratitude goggles are my favorite.
You see, they are the most colorful goggles of all!

Go ahead, try them on!
Now think about all the things you are grateful for...

You can also ask yourself, "Who am I grateful to?"
And take a moment to say thank you!

Think about how grateful you are for the sky...
then notice its beautiful shade of blue.
Think about how grateful you are for the
trees...then notice their bright green leaves.

Think about your delicious food, your comfy
house, your favorite toys...now these will all look
like a rainbow.

And when you think about the people you love,
and how grateful you are to have them
in your life, everything
will sparkle!

Think about your arms,
your legs, your eyes, and your voice
...and everything that makes you, you.

You are unique and wonderful,
just the way you are!

So take a minute to think...
What are you grateful for today?

Those gratitude goggles look amazing on you!
In fact, you can keep them.

And please remember to share them with others who may need more color in their lives.

About The Author

Andrea Mendoza-Vasconez, Ph.D. is an award-winning children's books author, a mother, a behavioral scientist, a teacher, an advocate, and a story-teller. Experiencing motherhood expanded her soul, enhancing her understanding of the importance of love, compassion, connection, and authenticity, which are recurring topics in her children's books. Andrea continuously seeks to cultivate these qualities through different resources, including books and workshops, which she eagerly shares with other parents through her website:

wholesomechildrenbooks.com.

About The Illustrator

Rita Nilson is a mother to two boys, a Ukrainian artist and illustrator, and a children's art teacher. Her unique perspective allows her to perceive miracles in the simplest of things, whether it be a sprouted apricot seed, a bird's nest discovered alongside her children in a hollow tree, or a delectable breakfast enjoyed to the backdrop of wonderful music. Through these seemingly insignificant moments, Rita nurtures a profound love and appreciation for God's creation, which is manifested in nature and other people.

Wholesome Children: Self-Awareness Series

The Wholesome Children: Self-Awareness book series is a guiding light for parents seeking to bond with their children over the values of kindness, compassion, gratitude, authenticity, and connection.

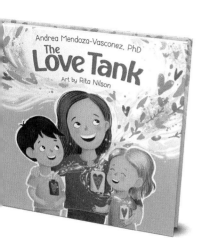

Other titles in this series:

The Love Tank:
Imagine you have a superpower container inside your body that fills up with love - A Love Tank! How do you feel when your love tank is full? What happens if it becomes empty? How can you help others to fill their love tank?

Made in the USA
Middletown, DE
15 December 2023

45919246R00018